What is Jazz?

What comes to mind when you think of jazz? Do you think of the cheerful, toe-tapping sound of Dixieland music or the slow, sad feeling of the blues? Perhaps Latin styles come to mind or Big Band swing music? Jazz is all of these and more. Born in America, jazz blended African, Latin, and European influences and it continues to evolve into a broad range of styles played around the world.

For you, the student pianist, jazz offers wonderful opportunities for self-expression through improvisation. Did you know that you improvise every day whenever you have a conversation? When you meet someone, you use your knowledge of words and language to make up a greeting right on the spot. In music, to improvise is to go beyond the notes that are written on the page. You use your knowledge of rhythm and melody to enhance existing music, create new music, and play it the way you think it should sound.

Jazz is rhythmic, upbeat, laid back, bluesy, exciting and cool, and you're going to have a lot of fun playing it!

Anatomy of a Jazz Chart

The information below explains some of the unique features of jazz charts (pieces).

Style Indication—describes the desired rhythmic feel or groove with particular regard to the timing of eighth notes, e.g., "Swing," "Latin," or "Rock."

Swing Equation—a reminder of how swing eighths should sound.

Chord Symbols—indicate harmony to aid improvisation. Chord symbols are placed over the top staff.

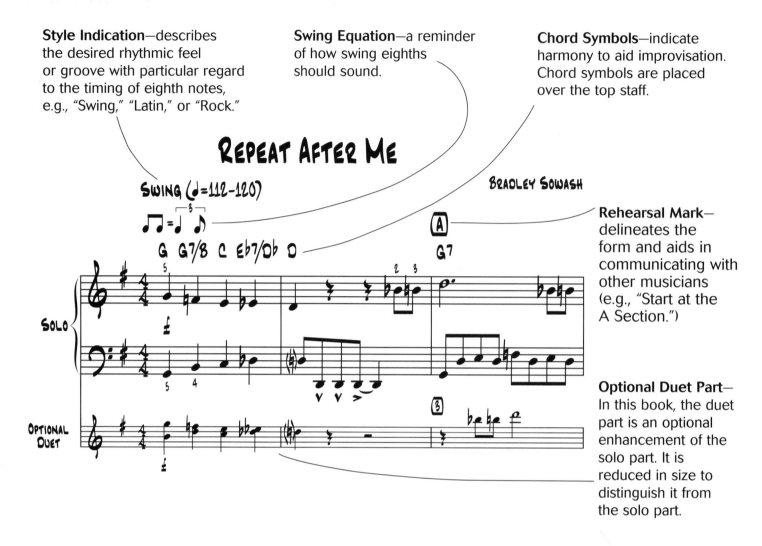

Rehearsal Mark—delineates the form and aids in communicating with other musicians (e.g., "Start at the A Section.")

Optional Duet Part—In this book, the duet part is an optional enhancement of the solo part. It is reduced in size to distinguish it from the solo part.

Jazz Piano Articulations

(notation)	short and separated
(notation)	hold full value
(notation)	loud, accented attack
(notation)	loud and short; accent and staccato combined
(notation)	first note longer and connected, second note staccato; sounds like "doo-wat"

Bradley Sowash

That's Jazz

book two performance
Walk the Talk

Contents

ISBN-10: 0-8497-9748-9
ISBN-13: 978-0-8497-9748-4

kjos Neil A. Kjos Music Company • Distributor

Welcome to the World of Jazz!

In the **That's Jazz** piano series, you will be introduced to jazz in the most enjoyable and efficient way — by playing it! Each book is a collection of tunes covering the main jazz styles of swing, ethnic, and rock. Each tune is followed by an optional *Going Further* page to introduce you to improvisation in its many forms. Additionally, optional duet parts are included to enhance the pieces and to encourage playing in groups. This series will guide you on your journey into jazz!

This book is for you if:

+ You want to get into jazz for the **first time**.
+ You want to play music by **ear**.
+ You want to have **fun** playing jazz tunes!
+ You want to learn skills that will help you become a **jazz pianist**.
+ You are studying or have previously studied its companion book, *That's Jazz, Book Two: Digging Deeper.*

How to Use *That's Jazz*

✦ Each tune in this book correlates to a preparatory tune in the companion method book, *That's Jazz, Book Two: Digging Deeper*. Whether learning through individual study or with a teacher, it is strongly recommended that serious jazz students master the preparatory tune before studying the correlating tune in this book. Refer to the Correlation Chart on page 6 for a complete overview.

✦ Piano teachers searching for a less rigorous approach to integrating jazz into their studios will find a treasure trove of resources here. Select tunes as supplemental music to traditional piano methods either individually or successively.

✦ At its most basic, this book is a collection of jazz tunes for performance.

1. The Tunes

Demonstration Tracks—*Listening* is imperative to developing jazz style. Visit the on-line multimedia library at www.kjos.com and follow the link to *That's Jazz* to hear and/or download performances and accompaniment tracks for the tunes found in this book.

Practice Suggestions—Begin by practicing each hand individually at a slow tempo. Increasing the tempo will come more easily when the individual parts are secure. Learn the tunes exactly as written, reserving improvisation for the *Going Further* pages (see below).

Enhanced Repeats—Jazz musicians often spontaneously enhance melodies by improvising variations. The written arrangements in this book emulate this practice. Therefore, look for differences such as altered rhythms or embellishments whenever a melody repeats near the end of a tune.

Duet Parts—Each tune in this book has an optional duet part. Although the solo parts were written to sound complete without them, the duet parts enhance the tunes, making lessons or playing with friends more interesting and fun. When possible, switching parts is a great way to better understand how the parts work together.

MIDI sounds—Each tune includes suggestions for optional MIDI sounds or "patches" for digital keyboards. Split points are given for instruments that allow two players to each use a unique sound on the same keyboard. If the parts overlap, the split point reads "none" indicating that two keyboards are needed for distinctive parts.

Steady Beat—The jazz tradition is steeped in rhythm. In jazz, maintaining an even pulse is far more important than playing all the right notes, so it's a good idea to practice with a metronome or drum machine accompaniment.

Chord Symbols—Jazz musicians often play from lead sheets that include only melody and chord symbols. Chord symbols facilitate improvisation and harmonic analysis even though the chords are written out. See the appendices in the back of the book for a list of chord symbols and their related chords.

2. *Going Further* Pages

The essence of jazz is improvisation. Each tune includes an important *Going Further* page designed to move you deeper into the world of jazz improvisation and personal expression. Take your time and avoid self-judgment as you learn and practice the jazz concepts presented here. Then, apply these new skills by taking the *Improv Challenge* that follows each *Going Further*. Finally, hang onto what you've learned so you can apply it to other tunes in the future.

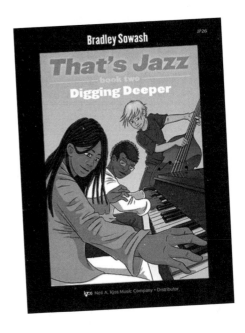

That's Jazz, Book Two

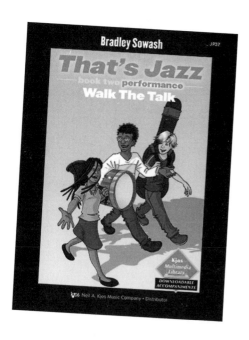

That's Jazz, Book Two - Performance

Correlation Chart

Use this chart as a guide when studying *That's Jazz, Book Two: Digging Deeper* together with *That's Jazz, Book Two – Performance: Walk the Talk.* The tunes are paired based on the improv skill presented in the *Going Further* pages.

Students and teachers may find it helpful to refer to each correlated tune in *That's Jazz, Book Two* for a more detailed explanation and review of the improv skills used in the *Going Further* pages of *That's Jazz, Book Two – Performance.*

Improv skill	Introduced in: **That's Jazz, Book Two**	Follow-up with: **That's Jazz, Book Two-** ***Performance***
Improvising with Chord Tones	*Take It for Granite* (p. 6)	*Jamaican Jam* (p. 7)
Improvising with Minor Scales	*History of Flight* (p. 11) *Major*	*Minor* *Day Dream* (p. 10)
Improvising with Dorian Patterns	*Flint and Steel* (p. 17)	*Already All Right* (p. 13)
Improvising with Pentatonic Scales	*Get Up, Get Ready* (p. 21)	*Rock Solid* (p. 17)
Improvising with Accumulation/Reduction and Blues Scales	*Math Whiz* (p. 31) and *Repeat After Me* (p. 37)	*Old Blue* (p. 20)
Improvising with Blues Scales	*Repeat After Me* (p. 37)	*Walk the Talk* (p. 23)
Enhancing Repeats	*Farmer's Market* (p. 43)	*Coyote Rock* (p. 26)

Jamaican Jam

Optional MIDI sounds: Solo (steel drums), Duet (elec. bass); Split point: B one 8ve below middle C

Bradley Sowash

Duet part one 8ve lower throughout

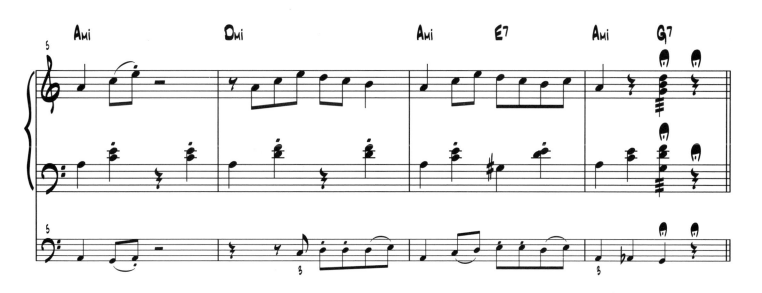

Use with That's Jazz, Book Two: pp. 6-10.

Jamaican Jam...Going Further

Chord Tones

In *Take It For Granite,* we discussed chords and inversions. Here we take it a step further by using different chord inversions as the basis for improvising.

1. Warm up on these chord inversions.
   The "licks" below are based on these chord tones.

2. Try this lick then make up your own.

3. Now warm up on these chord inversions.
   The "licks" below are based on these different inversions.

4. Try this lick then make up your own.

Improv Challenge

1. Play the A and B sections as written.
2. Repeat the A section, improvising a R.H. part that uses chord tones in different inversions. (Repeat the A section as many times as you like.)
3. End by playing the B and C sections as written.

Day Dream

Optional MIDI sounds: Solo (elec. piano), Duet (elec. piano); Split point: none

Bradley Sowash

Duet part one 8ve higher throughout

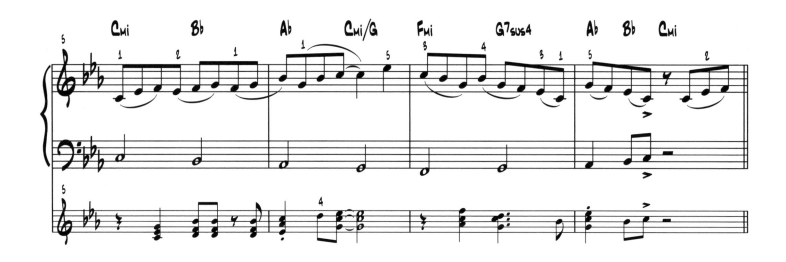

Use with That's Jazz, Book Two: pp. 11-16.

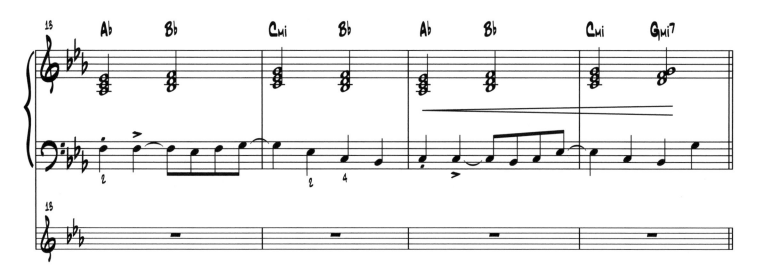

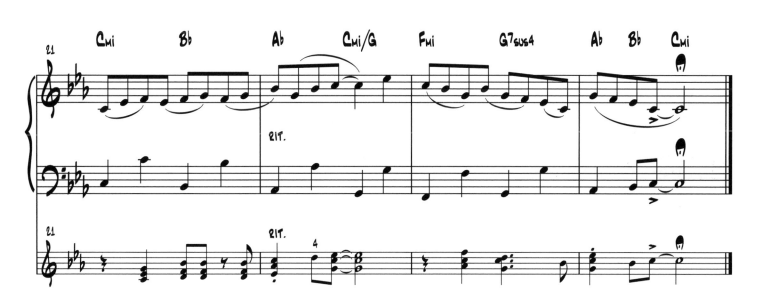

Day Dream…Going Further

Minor Scales

Use the ideas below to improvise over the bass line of *Day Dream*, using the C natural minor scale.

1. Change directions whenever you like.   Keep going!

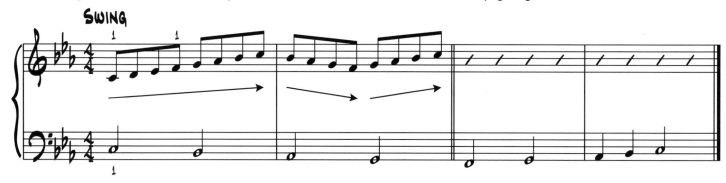

2. Add a few long notes.   Keep going!

3. Throw in some skips and leaps.   Keep going!

Improv Challenge

1. Play the A and B sections as written.
2. Repeat the A section, improvising a R.H. part with any of the guidelines above. Use the notated rhythms or make up your own. (Repeat the A section as many times as you like.)
3. End by playing the B and C sections as written.

Already All Right

Optional MIDI sounds: Solo (elec. piano), Duet (elec. bass); Split point: D# one 8ve below middle C

Bradley Sowash

Use with That's Jazz, Book Two: pp. 17-20.

Already All Right...Going Further

Dorian Patterns

Using *sequences* is a great way to improvise. To create a sequence - choose a pattern then start on a different note and repeat the pattern. The E Dorian scale works well with the chords in *Already All Right*.

E Dorian Scale

E Dorian Scale (or Mode)

1. Here is a three-note pattern followed by several sequences of that pattern. Varying the rhythm keeps it interesting.

2. Here is another three-note pattern with sequences.

3. Use any three notes of the E Dorian Scale to compose your own pattern and sequences.

Improv Challenge

1. Play sections A, B, and C as written.
2. Repeat the A section, improvising with Dorian patterns in the R.H. (Repeat the A section as many times as you like.)
3. End by playing the B section, C section, and Tag as written.

Rock Solid

Optional MIDI sounds: Solo (elec. piano), Duet (elec. bass); Split point: B one 8ve below middle C

Bradley Sowash

Use with That's Jazz, Book Two: pp. 21-24.

Rock Solid...Going Further

Pentatonic Scale

Rock Solid is in the key of D Major, but most of the melody uses a D minor pentatonic scale. The contrast gives it a gritty rock feel. Experiment with the notes below by playing various patterns and rhythms with just your right hand at first. When you're ready to put hands together, move on to example 1 below.

D Minor Pentatonic Scale

D Minor Pentatonic Scale

1. Here are a few ideas to get you started. Improvise on your own in the measures with the slashes. (Each slash represents one beat.)

Improv Challenge

1. Play the entire tune as written.
2. Repeat the A section, improvising a R.H. part in the A section using the D minor pentatonic scale. (Repeat the A section as many times as you like.)
3. End by playing the B section as written.

Old Blue

Optional MIDI sounds: Solo (vibes), Duet (bass); Split point: C♯ one octave below middle C

Bradley Sowash

Use after That's Jazz, Book Two: pp. 31-42.

Old Blue...Going Further

Bright Blues Scale/Accumulation and Reduction

Each key has its own associated bright blues scale. You can combine this scale with the concepts of accumulation and reduction to create a great blues improvisation.

F Bright Blues Scale

1. Use "accumulation" to build a lick from just a few notes to several.

2. Use "reduction" to reduce a lick from several notes to just a few.

Improv Challenge

1. Play the A section as written.
2. Repeat the A section, improvising a R.H. part using the bright blues scale and accumulation or reduction. (Repeat the A section as many times as you like.)
3. End by playing the B section as written.

Extra Challenge!

Play the duet part with your L.H. instead of the solo L.H. part! The trick to playing a walking bass while improvising is to keep your right hand licks simple. At first, use just half notes and quarter notes.

WALK THE TALK

Optional MIDI sounds: Solo (elec. piano), Duet (vibes); Split point: B above middle C

Bradley Sowash

Use with That's Jazz, Book Two: pp. 37-42.

Dark Blues Scale

The dark blues scale is like a relative minor to the bright blues scale. That's why it sounds so good in a minor blues like *Walk the Talk*.

D Dark Blues Scale

Play these licks as written then improvise your "responses" in the measures with the slashes. (Each slash represents one beat.)

Improv Challenge

1. Play the A section as written.
2. Repeat the A section, improvising a R.H. part using the dark blues scale. (Repeat the A section as many times as you like.)
3. End by playing the B section as written.

Coyote Rock

Optional MIDI sounds: Solo (elec. piano), Duet (elec. bass); Split point: A two 8ves below middle C

Bradley Sowash

Use with That's Jazz, Book Two: pp. 43-46.

Coyote Rock...Going Further

Enhanced Repeats

An exact repeat is a rare thing in jazz and rock styles. Below you'll find some ideas for enhancing the repeats in *Coyote Rock*.

1. Change the rhythm in the left hand.   2. Repeat notes in the melody.

3. Change chord inversions.   4. Use broken chords.

Tip: These are just a few of the possibilities for enhanced repeats. You could also change the rhythm of the melody, play it in a different octave or add more dynamics. Try these and experiment with your own ideas as well. Making choices will help you develop a personal musical style.

Improv Challenge

1. Play the A and B sections as written.
2. Enhance the repeat of these sections using some of the techniques shown above, or make up your own. (Repeat sections A and B as many times as you like.)
3. Play the C section as written.
4. End by enhancing the A section even more from the *D.S.* to the *Coda*.

Appendix A: Chord Glossary

Appendix B: Common Jazz Scales
and Associated Chords

Major Scales

C Major

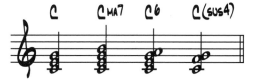

C Pentatonic (C Major minus the 4th and 7th)
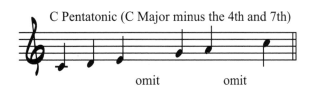

omit   omit

C Bright Blues (Pentatonic plus flat 3rd)

flat 3rd

C Mixolydian or Dominant Scale
(C Major with flat seventh)
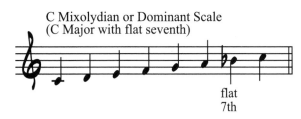

flat
7th

Minor Scales

A Natural Minor

A Minor Pentatonic
(Same notes as C Major Pentatonic)
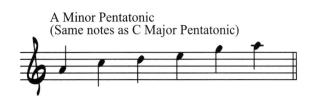

A Dark Blues

A Dorian
(A Natural Minor with raised sixth)
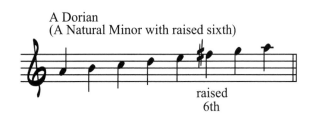

raised
6th

Appendix C: Seventh Chords

Triads (three note chords) are common to many types of music including jazz. However, harmonies with four (or more) notes such as these *seventh chords* are an essential part of most jazz styles.

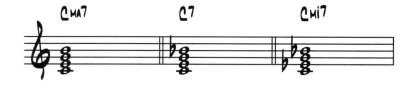

1. Here are three common types of seventh chords with their associated chord symbols: Cᴹᴬ7 (pronounced C major seven), C7 (C seven) and Cᴹⁱ7 (C minor seven).

2. We refer to these as seventh chords because they use the root, 3rd, 5th, and *7th* degrees of a scale.

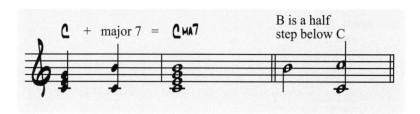

3. A handy way to distinguish seventh chords is to compare the 7th with the root. For example, Cᴹᴬ7 contains the notes, C, E, G, and B. The 7th (B) is a major seventh above the root (C), and when the root is transposed up an octave, it is a half step below. The chord symbol used in this book for a major 7th over a major triad is "ᴹᴬ7."

4. The 7th in this example is different from the previous example. C7 contains the notes C, E, G and B♭. B♭ is a minor seventh above the root, and when the root is transposed up the octave, it is a whole step below. The chord symbol for a minor 7th over a major triad is "7." This type of seventh chord is also referred to as a dominant seventh.

5. The 7th in this Cᴹⁱ7 chord is like the previous example because it is also a minor seventh above the root, and when the root is transposed up an octave, it is a whole step below. However, the triad below it is minor. The chord symbol used in this book for a minor 7th over a minor triad is "ᴹⁱ7."

6. Keep in mind that seventh chords can be played in various inversions. Every chord in this example is a Cᴹᴬ7 because each chord consists of the same notes (C, E, G, B).